WEATHER OR NOT

Today is Antoine's first day as a television weather forecaster. He is so nervous, he accidentally scrambled some of the words in his forecast. Can you help him clear up his cloudy delivery by unscrambling the words below?

The **stew** will have periods of **scinesloud,** followed by **inra.** It could get very **krad** at night, with **thlig** coming in the morning.

If a **tradoon** springs up in the south, we **loduc** be in for quite a **nurt.** The **trannefoo** should see patchy **posts,** so if your **potss** need **chapnigt,** now is a **odog emit** for it.

Northern **reasa** should **looc** tonight, after a **ghih epuratemtre** of 85 **greesed.** There's a ridge of **urdenth** and **nightling** pressing through, so **nagh** out all your wrinkled **lecoths.**

Answer on page 47.

LABORATORY LABYRINTH

Dr. Zarkoff is up to his old tricks. As the final ingredient for his energy shakes, he's dropping this grape into the beaker. Unfortunately, the piping and tubes are so jumbled, he's not sure if the grape will ever come out. See if you can follow the tubes around to let the doctor know where the grape will end up. Hint: In Dr. Zarkoff's maze, a funnel will catch any grape dropped into it, and the grape will then continue on.

ENERGY SHAKE

MOW, HOWARD

Can you find at least 12 differences between
these two pictures of Howard's mowing service?

Illustrated by Anni Matsick

DOT MAGIC

Hurry, hurry! Step right up. Connect these dots to see the newest attraction at the Bumbling Brothers Circus.

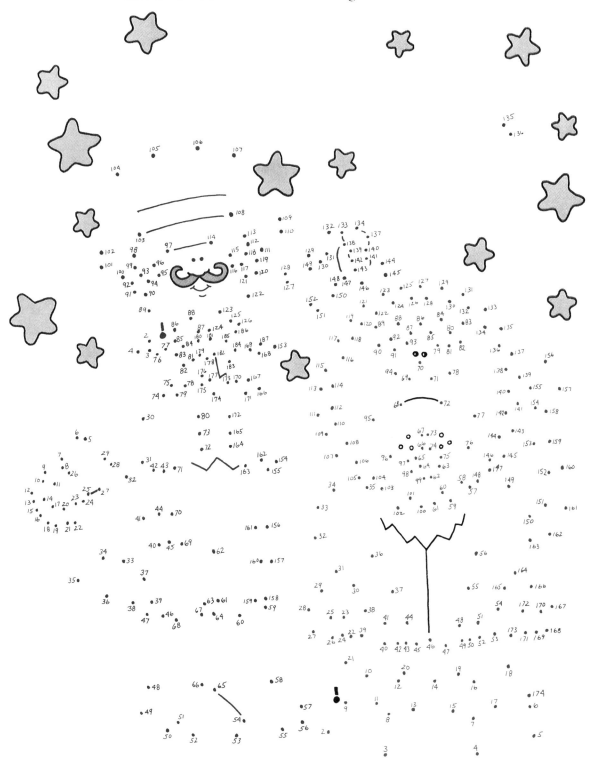

VEGETABLE PATCHWORK

Rebus Rita planted a garden in her backyard. She couldn't afford to hire a scarecrow, so she used a rebus to confuse the birds and to mark out what she had planted. See if you can read the signs to guess what Rebus Rita is growing.

ENGINE WORK

Melissa and Mandy are helping their dad work on his car. He's showing them all the different engine parts, along with other things about autos. Fifty-eight words about four-wheeled vehicles can fit into the boxes on the next page. Cross each word off the list as you find where it belongs and this car will soon be running smoothly. One word has been filled in to get you started.

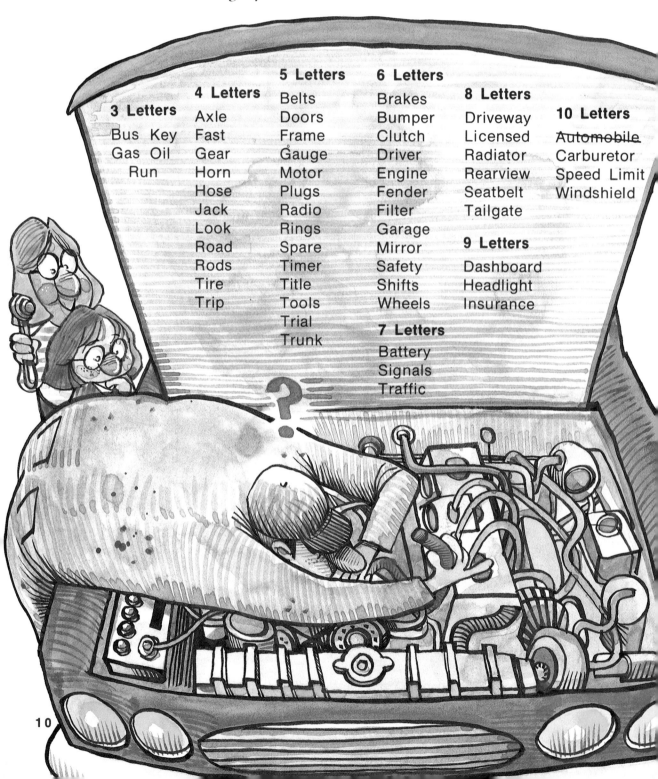

3 Letters
Bus Key
Gas Oil
Run

4 Letters
Axle
Fast
Gear
Horn
Hose
Jack
Look
Road
Rods
Tire
Trip

5 Letters
Belts
Doors
Frame
Gauge
Motor
Plugs
Radio
Rings
Spare
Timer
Title
Tools
Trial
Trunk

6 Letters
Brakes
Bumper
Clutch
Driver
Engine
Fender
Filter
Garage
Mirror
Safety
Shifts
Wheels

7 Letters
Battery
Signals
Traffic

8 Letters
Driveway
Licensed
Radiator
Rearview
Seatbelt
Tailgate

9 Letters
Dashboard
Headlight
Insurance

10 Letters
Automobile
Carburetor
Speed Limit
Windshield

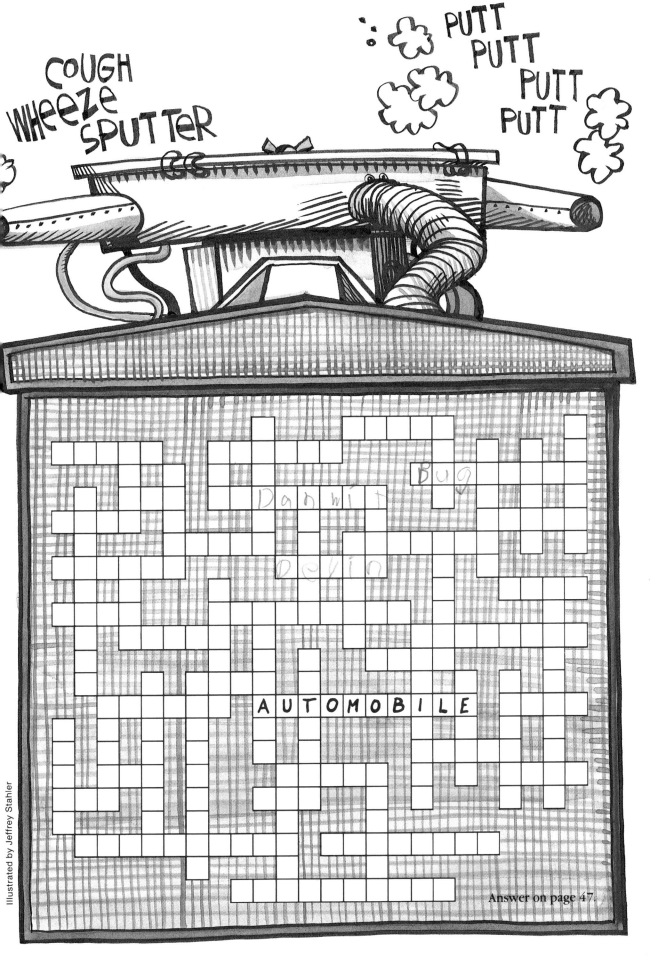

Answer on page 47.

Illustrated by Jeffrey Stahler

STOP, LOOK, AND LIST

Under every category list one thing that begins with each letter. For example, one water vehicle that begins with "S" is Sailboat. See if you can name another.

Water Vehicles

S _____

B _____

C _____

F _____

H _____

Campfire Foods

S _____

B _____

C _____

F _____

H _____

Farm Things

S _____

B _____

C _____

F _____

H _____

Illustrated by Lisa Dayer

Answer on page 48.

FIREHOUSE MEMORIES
Part 1

Take a long look at this picture. Try to remember everything you see in it. Then turn the page, and try to answer some questions about it without looking back.

Illustrated by John Nez

DON'T READ THIS UNTIL YOU HAVE LOOKED AT "Firehouse Memories—Part 1" ON PAGE 13.

FIREHOUSE MEMORIES

Part 2

Can you answer these questions about the firehouse scene you saw? Don't peek!

1. Which fire company was in this scene?
2. What were the firefighters doing to the truck?
3. Which firefighter has his name on his shirt?
4. What color were his suspenders?
5. How many helmets were in the picture?
6. How many lengths of hose were stretched out?
7. Who was wearing boots?
8. Where was the dog sleeping?
9. How many birds were in the scene?
10. Where was the pay telephone?

Answer on page 48.

UNDERCOVER ANIMALS

Two animals are hidden below. To find out which animals they are, fill in the spaces under each letter with the letter that comes before it in alphabetical order. When you're done, you should have uncovered the names of these animals on the second and bottom rows.

S B D D P P O

_ _ _ _ _ _ _

H J S B G G F

_ _ _ _ _ _ _

Illustrated by Gregg Valley

Answer on page 48.

SQUARE SHARE

All the equations in these squares share some of the same numbers. By using the numbers shown and following the math signs, see if you can figure out what numbers belong in the empty boxes. Be careful, because some tricky three-part equations equal other three-part equations.

Answer on page 48.

	+		=			2	x		=	2
+		÷		−		x		x		+
	x	4	+	4	=		−	5	+	
=		x		=		=		+		=
3	x		=	6		14	−		=	
		=						=		
	÷		=	2		10	−		=	2
−		x		+		−		+		+
5	x	2	−		=	6	−	2	−	
=		−		=		=		+		=
5	+		=	11			+		=	

GLOBE PROBE

Cincinnati Holmes, that world famous adventurer, needed a guide to lead him to the fabulous hidden cities. Cincy showed the guide, whose name was Sherpa, the countries he wanted to visit. But Sherpa only remembered the countries by their former names. So Cincy had to use his trusty map to figure out the current names of the countries where the cities are hidden.

   The countries are pictured here as shown on the map. Beside each country is a name it was known by in the past. See if you can find each country on the map and write its current name in the blank.

1.   Gaul

_____

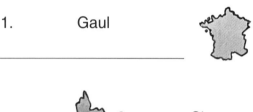

2.   Siam

_____

3.   British Honduras

_____

4.   Persia

_____

5.   Hispaniola

_____

6. Southern Rhodesia

_____

7.   Mesopotamia

_____

Canada

United States

Cuba

Belize

Dominican Republic

Venezuela

Trinidad

Guyana

Panama

Colombia

Ecuador

Brazil

Peru

Bolivia

Paraguay

Chile

Argentina

Uruguay

Illustrated by John Nez

8.   Formosa

_____

9.   Zaire

_____

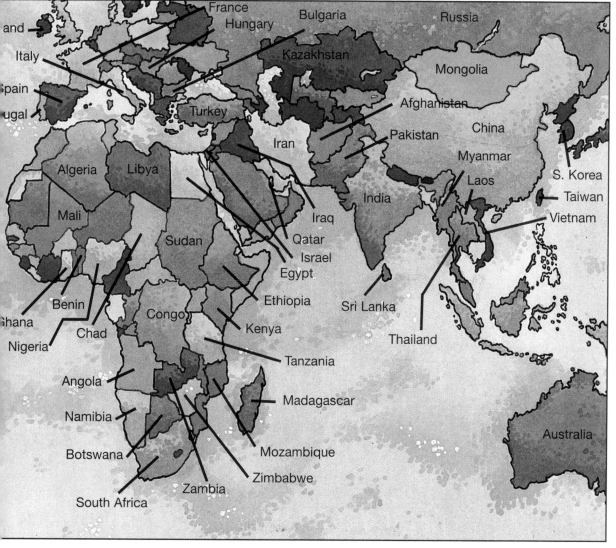

Answer on page 50.   PUZZLEMANIA **17**

ODD ONE OUT

One item in each set doesn't belong with the other three. Circle that item and write its first letter in the numbered space at the bottom. When you're finished, you should have written three new words that do belong together.

Answer on page 48.

1. penny   bank   dime   quarter
2. street   road   lane   river
3. orange   lemonade   milk   juice
4. wings   owl   beak   feathers
5. ship   sailboat   kite   canoe
6. cherry   stop sign   tomato   cloud
7. fish   rabbit   seal   eel
8. egg   apple   pear   orange
9. car   van   elephant   truck
10. fork   key   knife   spoon
11. couch   sofa   bed   sink
12. April   Thursday   May   March
13. rose   daisy   tulip   rake
14. tire   windshield   eye   horn
15. apple   ice   snow   frost
16. pound   mile   ounce   ton

$\overline{}$ $\overline{}$ $\overline{}$ $\overline{}$ $\overline{}$ $\overline{}$ $\overline{}$ $\overline{}$ $\overline{}$ $\overline{}$
1   2   3   4   5   6   7   8   9   10

$\overline{}$ $\overline{}$ $\overline{}$ $\overline{}$ $\overline{}$ $\overline{}$
11 12 13 14 15 16

Illustrated by Melvin Conrad

FLOAT FUN

It's the Homecoming Parade and the art class has taken first prize for its wonderful float. The only problem is no one is quite sure what their float is. Use your imagination to draw in what you think the winning parade float should be.

WHAT'S BUGGING YOU?

On warm nights, Jenny and Jerome like to catch fireflies in their backyard. They've gotten quite good at finding all sorts of bugs. Can you find all the insects and arachnids that are waiting on the screen door? Look across, backward, up, down, and diagonally to catch them all. Once you've caught all the bugs on the list, look for the letters B-U-G and see how many times you can find a "BUG."

Ant	Dragonfly	Katydid	Praying Mantis
Aphid	Firefly	Lacewing	Pupa
Beetle	Flea	Ladybug	Scorpion
Bumblebee	Fruitfly	Larva	Spider
Butterfly	Gnat	Locust	Termite
Caterpillar	Grasshopper	Louse	Tick
Centipede	Grub	Mite	Walking Stick
Cicada	Honeybee	Mosquito	Wasp
Cockroach	Hornet	Moth	Waterbug
Cricket	Housefly	Mud Dauber	

Illustrated by Terry Rogers

W O K C I T S G N I K L A W T A R
A L A V B U G U B U M B L E B E E
T E T I M R E T B U G M K O P F E
E T Y L F R E T T U B C O P R G E
R I D F W M O S Q U I T O T N H B
B M I D I C G X T R L H S A H C Y
U R D R G R I U C I S U T S B A E
G A C A B U E C B S C O R P I O N
U L E G U B B F A O W K P I M R O
B L N O G J U R L D D F U D U K H
S I T N A M G N I Y A R P E D C O
P P I F B U G T W Z V U A R D O R
A R P L B B L A C E W I N G A C N
V E E Y U E S U O L G T K B U G E
R T D G A P H I D U N F G U B B T
A A E L F R G U B A E L T E E B Z
L C X T H O U S E F L Y M G R U B

Answer on page 48.

ROCKING WRONG

How many things can you find wrong in this picture?

FAVORITE BOOKS

Every Saturday morning, Samantha and three of her friends go to the library. Each friend likes to read a different kind of book (biography, mystery, adventure, or western) and each reaches the library in a different way (by car, bus, bicycle, or walking). From the clues, can you figure out how each person reaches the library and what kind of book each reader likes?

Use the chart to keep track of your answers. Put an X in each box that can't be true and a circle in the boxes where information is true. For example, clue 2 says that a boy rides his bicycle. Since this means the girls don't go by bicycle, put an X in the boxes by the girls' names under the bicycle column.

	Bus	Walking	Bicycle	Car	Biography	Mystery	Adventure	Western
Samantha								
Darrin								
Endora								
Maurice								

Answer on page 48.

1. Of the four friends, Samantha is older than Darrin, but younger than Maurice, who is not the oldest.
2. The boy who rides his bicycle likes to read true stories of famous people.
3. One girl likes mysteries, while the older boy, who walks to the library, prefers western stories.
4. The oldest child takes the bus and doesn't like mysteries.

Illustrated by Terry Rogers

HIDDEN PICTURES

There are at least 25 objects hidden in this picture. How many can you find?

MUMMY'S THE WORD

After a rough 4000 year sleep, these mummies awoke to find themselves a bit knotted. Can you match which scepter belongs to which mummy by untangling their wrappings?

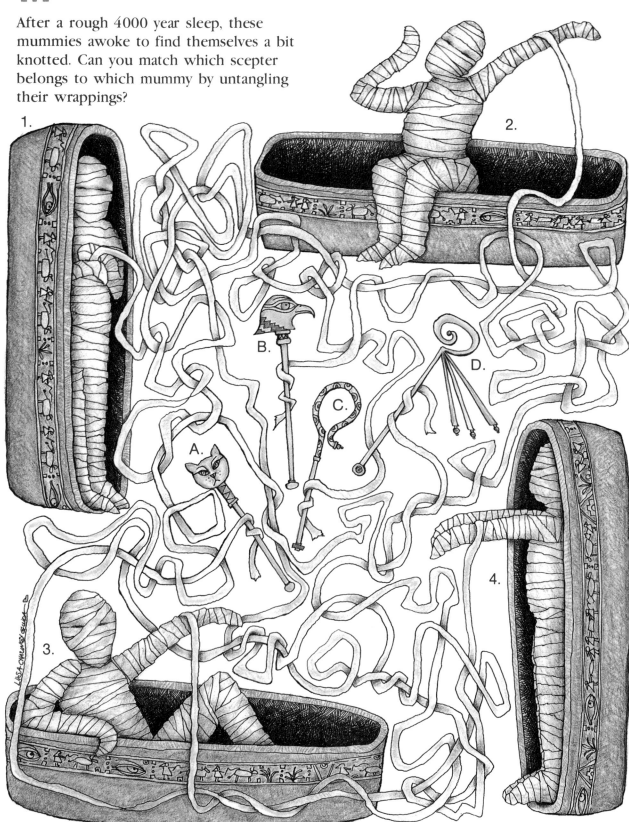

1.

2.

B.

A.

C.

D.

3.

4.

Answer on page 48.

PIN-UP PAGE

Can you pin down some new words by filling in the spaces below? Don't get stuck as you use the clues to find out which words contain all these PINs.

1. Twirl a top: ___ pin

2. Type of evergreen tree: pin ___

3. Mixture of red and white: pin ___

4. Measure of ice cream: pin ___

5. One of Columbus's ships: Pin ___ ___

6. Spotted horse or type of bean: pin ___ ___

7. Decorative figure hung from

   the ceiling at children's parties: piñ ___ ___ ___

8. A crab's claw: pin ___ ___ ___

9. Green leafy vegetable: ___ pin ___ ___ ___

10. Arcade game: pin ___ ___ ___ ___

11. Buying things and spending money: ___ ___ ___ ___ pin___

12. Table tennis: Pin ___ - ___ ___ ___ ___

13. A freshwater turtle: ___ ___ ___ ___ ___ pin

14. The absolute top, the peak: pin ___ ___ ___ ___ ___

15. A sweet tropical fruit: pin ___ ___ ___ ___ ___

16. Puppet who wanted to be a real boy: Pin ___ ___ ___ ___ ___ ___

Illustrated by Gregg Valley

Answer on page 49.

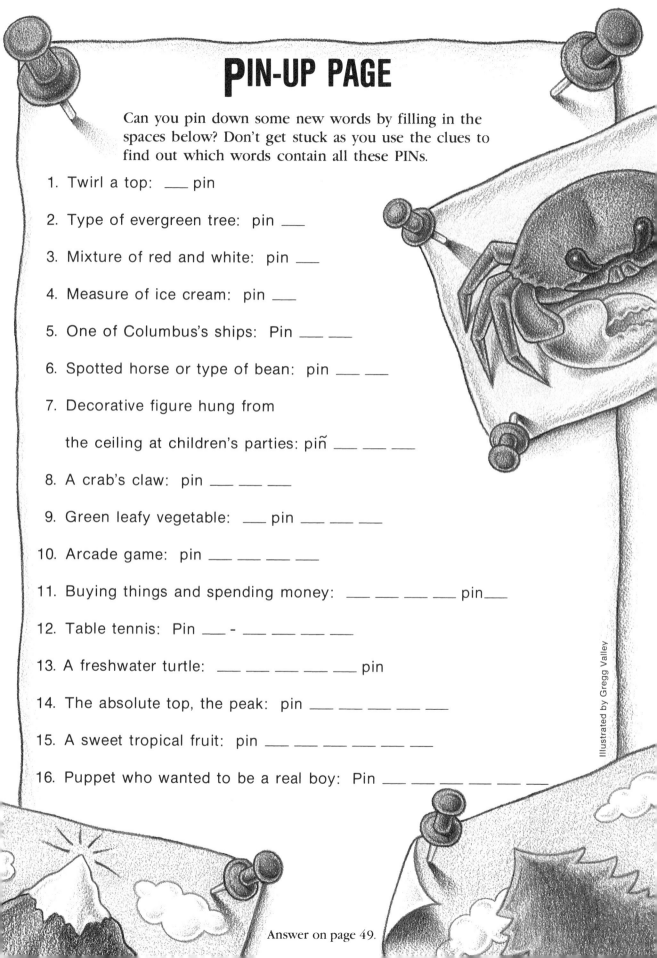

THE CASE OF THE PILFERED PINE

See if you can solve this mystery. Read the story and
fill in the missing words. Then match the numbered
letters with the corresponding spaces at the end of
the story. If you've filled in the spaces correctly,
you'll discover what became of the little pine.

A cold December __ __ __ __ was blowing. The sky was covered with
        14

gray __ __ __ __ __ __ , and white flakes of __ __ __ __ were
     11   19

beginning to fall. Sally Squirrel was happy, though, as she flipped her bushy

__ __ __ __ and ran across the field to visit her friend, the little pine tree.
16 1

Every day she had climbed the tree's sturdy __ __ __ __ __ and played in
                                              6   9

its swaying __ __ __ __ __ __ __ __ . She loved its dark
            2

__ __ __ __ __ color and the smell of the sharp pine __ __ __ __ __ __ __ .
      3   22

But today something was wrong! The little pine tree was gone! All that

remained was a stump.

"Someone has stolen my __ __ __ __ !" cried Sally, and her eyes filled with
                        20

__ __ __ __ __ __ . "Oh, Sammy Snowbird, please help me __ __ __ __
   4 13   8

out where my favorite tree has gone."

"I'll try," chirped __ __ __ __ __ , and he flew away into the gray
                    17

__ __ __ .
15

28 PUZZLEMANIA   Illustrated by Margeaux Lucas

It was getting dark by the time Sammy returned with good news for Sally.

"I think I've found your friend," he called. "Just __ __ __ __ __ __ me!"
                                                              10

Off they went through the snow until they came to a small __ __ __ __ __ with
                                                                          5

a bright candle in the front __ __ __ __ __ __ . Sally crept forward and
                               7

peeped inside. She saw four people in front of a warm fireplace—a mother, a

father, and two __ __ __ __ __ __ __ __ . How happy they all seemed.
                 12   21

"Look over in the corner," said Sammy, who was perched near her. "Isn't

that your friend? I think it's very __ __ __ __ __ here."
                                      18

Sally looked, and she gasped with amazement at what she saw in one

corner of the living room.

"That's my __ __ __ __ tree all right. I'm so glad to know what's
             23

become of it."

What did Sally see in the corner?

__ __ __ __ __ __ __ __ __ __
 1 2 3 4 5 6 7 8 9 10

__ __ __ __ __ __ __ __ __ __ __ __ __
11 12 13 14 15 16 17 18 19 20 21 22 23

Answer on page 49.

PICTURE MIXER

Copy these mixed-up squares in the spaces on the next page to put this picture back together. The letters and numbers tell you where each square belongs. The first one, A-3, has been done for you.

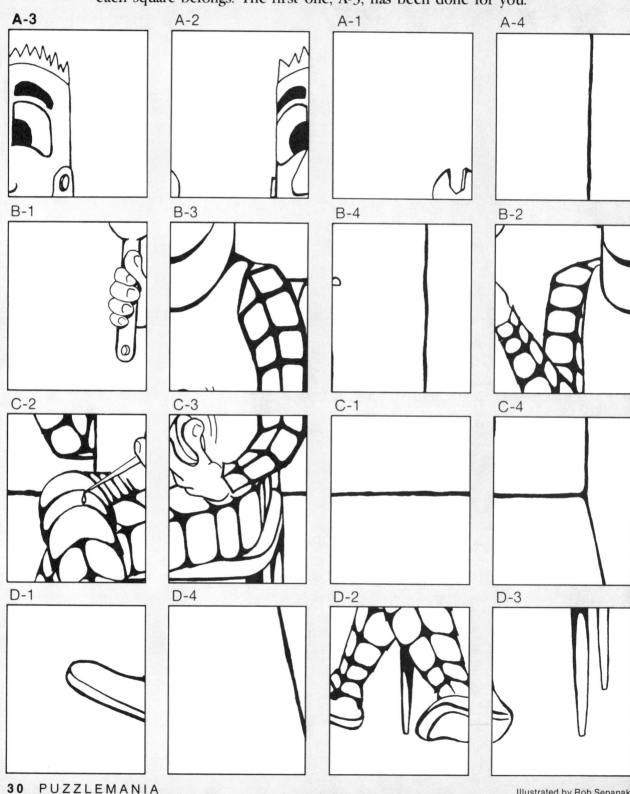

Illustrated by Rob Sepanak

	1	2	3	4
A				
B				
C				
D				

ICE-CREAM CODES

At Ira's Ice-Cream Igloo, they're always trying new riddles on their customers. Anyone who can figure out Ira's message gets free sprinkles on his or her ice cream. See if you can use the menu below to decipher Ira's latest riddle.

Illustrated by R. Michael Palan

HOW DO YOU

LEARN TO WORK

IN AN ICE-

CREAM PARLOR ?

YOU GO TO

SUNDAY SCHOOL.

PLUS FUSS

This puzzle has plenty of pluses that will add up to fun. Give yourself an A plus if you find at least 26 addition symbols hidden in this scene.

Illustrated by John Nez

WHAT'S IN A WORD?

For every tree that is chopped down, good lumberjacks plant a new tree so forests can continue to grow. There are a lot of smaller words planted in the letters of LUMBERJACKS, like BACK and JACK. How many words of three letters or more, without using plurals that end in s, can you find growing in LUMBERJACKS?

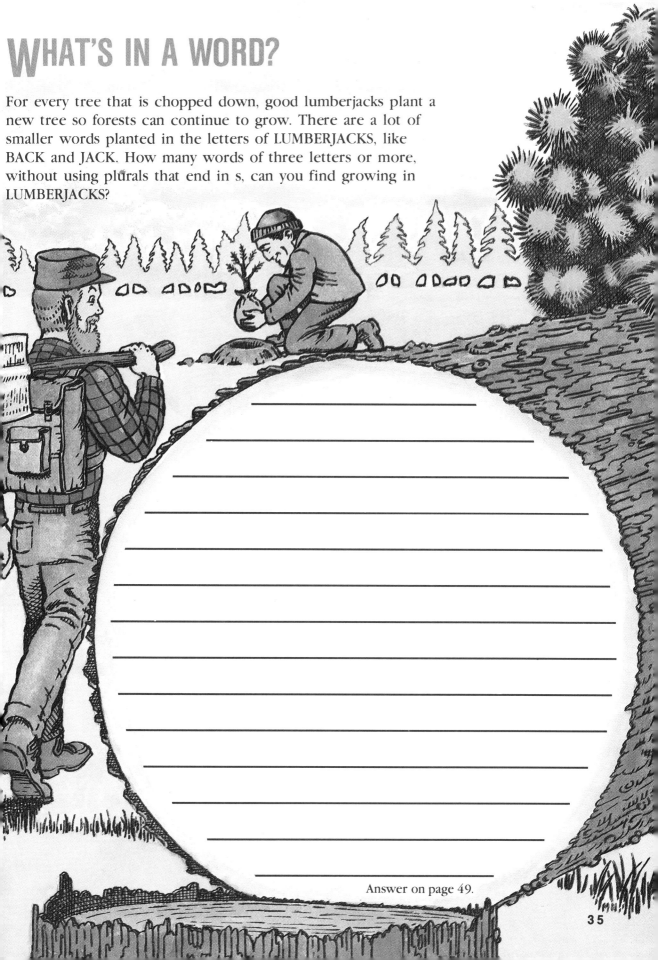

Answer on page 49.

FLORAL FEATURES

In bright sunlight, the features of these flowers all look the same. To add a little color to them, fill in as many of the words as you can. Working on all the words will help you discover what missing color will fill in each blossom.

I Across

3. Name tag
7. Beside, near
8. Want ___
10. ___, myself and I
11. Mystery color of this flower
13. Gas engines
15. Signal for help
16. Acorn producer
17. _____ Christmas!

Down

1. What birds do
2. Not she
4. First letter of the alphabet
5. Root vegetable
6. After "sol" and before "ti"
7. To ___ or not
9. Where a student works
11. Snow White's sister, _____ Red
12. Entrance
13. Pop's mate
14. What the sun sends out
18. Registered Nurse (abbreviation)

II Across

1. Shove
5. Afternoon (abbreviation)
7. Buddy
9. _____ _____ (2 words) little teapot
11. Mystery color of this flower
13. Eenie _____ minie mo
15. What burns your feet at the beach (2 words)
16. Opposite of out
17. The earth revolves around the _____

Down

2. Not down
3. Happy facial expressions
4. Give money for service
6. Cutting wood
8. Sour fruit
10. _____ Lisa (famous painting)
12. Permit
14. Nickname for Edward
15. Short greeting

III Across

2. Elm, for example
5. Exclamation
7. Go bananas over something
9. Carpet
11. Short for animal doctor
12. Mystery color of this flower
14. Long, thin vegetable
16. Spot on a carpet
19. Mailed

Down

1. Make a mistake
3. Roof edge
4. Tied, as in a sport score
5. Either this _____ that
6. Very large
8. Extraterrestrial (abbreviation)
10. What makes a lawn
13. Go in
15. Upon
17. I have _____ apple
18. Beat _____ !

Answer on page 49.

Illustrated by Barbara Gray

37

HOME, SWEET HOME

Can you number these pictures to tell what happened first, second, and so on?

Answer on page 50.

Illustrated by Jon Davis

KEVIN'S KITCHEN

Kevin is cooking dinner for some friends. To find out what the main course will be, fill in the names of each pictured item on the numbered lines. When you finish, the yellow column will reveal the meal.

1. ___ ___ ___ ___ ___

2. ___ ___ ___ ___ ___

3. ___ ___ ___ ___ ___

4. ___ ___ ___ ___ ___

5. ___ ___ ___ ___ ___ ___ ___ ___

6. ___ ___ ___ ___

7. ___ ___ ___ ___

Answer on page 50.

Basso

39

BL BLISS

Without bluffing, see how many things you can find on these pages that begin with the blended BL sound. Work slowly and don't blink. If you miss one, you'll be blue.

bleat

BLUEBERRIES

ROW, ROW, ROW

Each dog has something in common with the two others in the same row. In the top row across, each dog is barking. Look at the other rows across, down, and diagonally. What's the same about each row of three?

Illustrated by Liisa Chauncy Guida

Answer on page 50.

INSTANT PICTURE

To see who's looking up, fill in every space that has two dots.

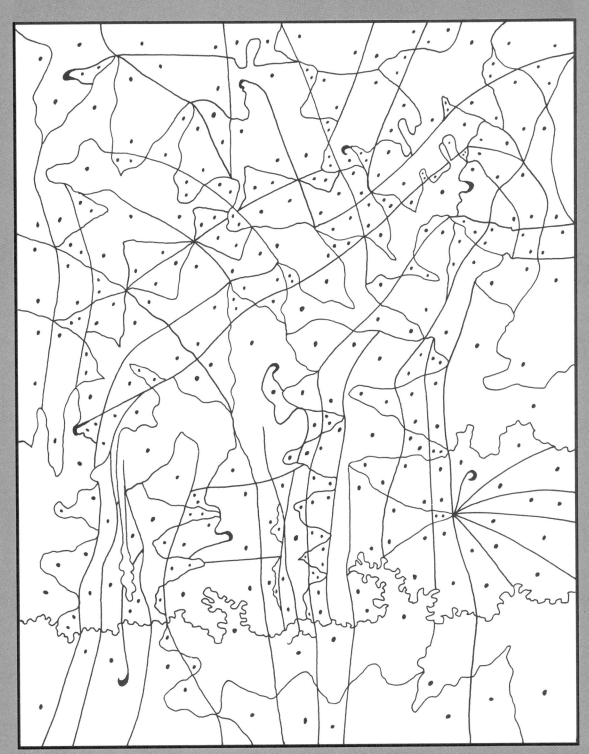

Illustrated by Rob Sepanak

Answer on page 50.

HORROR IN THE OPERA

Oh no! This is horrible! It's the opening night of the opera season and everyone is here. But Mrs. Gold and Mrs. Silver have appeared wearing the exact same outfits. Can you pick out these two ladies before anyone else does? Remember, it's the clothes and jewelry that match, even though the women are different.

Illustrated by R. Michael Palan

Answer on page 50.

WHO AM I?

Can you guess the answer before you reach the last clue?

1. Several versions of my story have been told many times throughout the centuries.

2. I am a fictional character who may have been based on a real person who lived in Wales during the sixth century.

3. Some versions of stories about me claim I sailed to Avalon at the end of my life.

4. Some stories claim I will someday return, thus giving me the title "The Once and Future King."

5. My downfall was caused by my enemy, Modred (some say we were related).

6. I am a legendary English king from the Middle Ages.

7. According to one legend, I gained the throne of England by pulling the sword Excalibur from a stone after many others had tried and failed.

8. I established my court in Camelot, and gathered together the bravest men, who became the Knights of the Round Table.

Who Am I?

Answer on page 50.

ANSWERS

COVER

WEATHER OR NOT (page 3)

The **west** will have periods of **cloudiness,** followed by **rain.** It could get very **dark** at night, with **light** coming in the morning.

If a **tornado** springs up in the south, we **could** be in for quite a **turn.** The **afternoon** should see patchy **spots,** so if your **spots** need **patching,** now is a **good time** for it.

Northern **areas** should **cool** tonight, after a **high temperature** of 85 **degrees.** There's a ridge of **thunder** and **lightning** pressing through, so **hang** out all your wrinkled clothes.

LABORATORY LABYRINTH (pages 4-5)

DOT MAGIC (page 7)

VEGETABLE PATCHWORK (pages 8-9)

1. collie + flower = cauliflower
2. bee + t + s = beets
3. two + May + toes = tomatoes
4. pump + kin = pumpkin
5. sell + er + e = celery
6. s + pin + itch = spinach
7. on + yun = onion
8. ra + dish = radish
9. pot + eight o's = potatoes
10. egg + plant = eggplant
11. k + horn = corn
12. car + rots = carrots
13. b + rock + coil + e = broccoli

ENGINE WORK (pages 10-11)

```
              G      MOTOR           W
TOOLS    BRAKES      O   C  R  H
     O   P  U  R        TAILGATE
  D  OIL  SEATBELT      D  U  D  E
JACK   U     G  U  I       TRIAL
  S    GAUGE  M  TRAFFIC   O   S
SHIFTS      SPARE     I  H
  B    A    M     E  V    L   HOSE
RODS        INSURANCE  T     P
  A  TIMER  I       K   REARVIEW
  R      R  G  B    GEAR      E
  D    L  HORN A       D  B  S  D
   DRIVER AUTOMOBILE    AXLE
R    O   C  A  L  T     A  L  F  I
I    O   E  D  S  E     T ITLE  M
N    RUN  L     F RAME  O  S  TRIP
GAS      E  KEY  N  S   R   Y  T
S        E  G    N      G
    WINDSHIELD DRIVEWAY
          T    E  N
       CARBURETOR
```

STOP, LOOK, AND LIST (page 12)
Here are our answers. You may have found others.

Water Vehicles	Campfire Foods
Submarine	Stew
Boat	Beans
Canoe	Coffee
Ferry	Fish
Hydrofoil	Hot Dogs

Farm Things
Silo
Barn
Chicken Coop
Fields
Hay

FIREHOUSE MEMORIES (page 14)
1. Hook & Ladder No. 1
2. Polishing it
3. Big Ed
4. Green
5. Two
6. Two
7. The female firefighter in front
8. Under the truck
9. Four
10. On the wall out front to the right

UNDERCOVER ANIMALS (page 14)

S B D D P P O

R A C C O O N

H J S B G G F

G I R A F F E

SQUARE SHARE (page 15)

2	+	8	=	10		2	x	1	=	2
+		÷		-		x		x		+
1	x	4	+	4	=	7	-	5	+	6
=		x				=		+		=
3	x	2	=	6		14	-	6	=	8
		=						=		
10	÷	5	=	2		10	-	8	=	2
		x		+		-		+		+
5	x	2	-	9	=	6	-	2	=	3
=		-		=		=		+		=
5	+	6	=	11		4	+	1	=	5

GLOBE PROBE (pages 16-17)
This answer appears on page 50.

ODD ONE OUT (page 18)
1. bank
2. river
3. orange
4. owl
5. kite
6. cloud
7. rabbit
8. egg
9. elephant
10. key
11. sink
12. Thursday
13. rake
14. eye
15. apple
16. mile

B	R	O	O	K		C	R	E	E	K		S	T	R	E	A	M
1	2	3	4	5		6	7	8	9	10		11	12	13	14	15	16

WHAT'S BUGGING YOU? (pages 20-21)

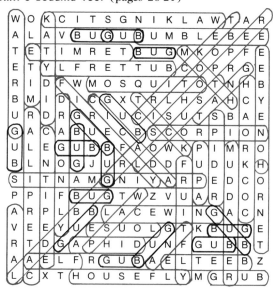

There are 16 loose BUGs on this screen.

FAVORITE BOOKS (page 23)
From clue 1, we know the age levels of all four people. Samantha is older than Darrin, but Maurice is older than both of them. However, he is not the oldest, so that only leaves Endora. Clue 4 says the oldest child, which is Endora, takes the bus, but doesn't like mysteries. Since a girl likes mysteries (clue 3), that must be Samantha.

Clue 3 says the older boy, Maurice, walks and likes westerns. So the boy who rides his bike and likes biographies (clue 2) must be Darrin.

By elimination, Endora must like adventure stories, while Samantha must reach the library by car.

	Bus	Walking	Bicycle	Car	Biography	Mystery	Adventure	Western
Samantha	X	X	X	O	X	O	X	X
Darrin	X	X	O	X	O	X	X	X
Endora	O	X	X	X	X	X	O	X
Maurice	X	O	X	X	X	X	X	O

MUMMY'S THE WORD (page 26)
A-2
B-3
C-1
D-4

PIN-UP PAGE (page 27)

1. spin
2. pine
3. pink
4. pint
5. Pinta
6. pinto
7. piñata
8. pincer
9. spinach
10. pinball
11. shopping
12. Ping-Pong
13. terrapin
14. pinnacle
15. pineapple
16. Pinocchio

THE CASE OF THE PILFERED PINE (pages 28-29)

A cold December WIND was blowing. The sky was covered with gray CLOUDS, and white flakes of SNOW were beginning to fall. Sally Squirrel was happy, though, as she flipped her bushy TAIL and ran across the field to visit her friend, the little pine tree. Every day she had climbed the tree's sturdy TRUNK and played in its swaying BRANCHES. She loved its dark GREEN color and the smell of the sharp pine NEEDLES.

But today something was wrong! The little pine tree was gone! All that remained was a stump.

"Someone has stolen my TREE!" cried Sally, and her eyes filled with TEARS. "Oh, Sammy Snowbird, please help me FIND out where my favorite tree has gone."

"I'll try," chirped SAMMY, and he flew away into the gray SKY.

It was getting dark by the time Sammy returned with good news for Sally. "I think I've found your friend," he called. "Just FOLLOW me!"

Off they went through the snow until they came to a small HOUSE with a bright candle in the front WINDOW. Sally crept forward and peeped inside. She saw four people in front of a warm fireplace—a mother, a father, and two CHILDREN. How happy they all seemed.

"Look over in the corner," said Sammy, who was perched near her. "Isn't that your friend? I think it's very HAPPY here."

Sally looked, and she gasped with amazement at what she saw in one corner of the living room.

"That's my PINE tree all right. I'm so glad to know what's become of it."

What did Sally see in the corner?

```
 A   B E A U T I F U L
 1   2 3 4 5 6 7 8 9 10

 C  H  R  I  S  T  M  A  S    T  R  E  E
11 12 13 14 15 16 17 18 19   20 21 22 23
```

PICTURE MIXER (pages 30-31)

ICE-CREAM CODES (pages 32-33)

How do you learn to work in an ice-cream parlor? You go to Sundae School.

WHAT'S IN A WORD? (page 35)

Here are the words we found. You may have found others.

able	camel	lace	ramble
ace	car	lack	real
alum	care	lake	rebus
amber	case	lamb	rule
amble	cause	lame	rumble
arc	clear	lark	ruse
are	cram	laser	sable
ark	cruel	leak	sack
arm	crumb	luck	sale
bale	curb	lure	same
bar	cure	mace	scale
bare	curl	make	scar
bark	ear	male	scare
bear	earl	marble	sea
blame	elm	mare	seal
blare	jab	mask	sear
blur	jam	meal	slack
brace	jamb	muck	slam
bum	jar	mule	slumber
cab	jerk	race	slur
cable	jumble	rack	smack
cake	kale	rake	smear
came	lab	ram	use

FLORAL FEATURES (pages 36-37)

HOME SWEET HOME (page 38)

5 3
6 4
2 1

KEVIN'S KITCHEN (page 39)

1. T A B L E
2. A P R O N
3. S P O O N S
4. C H A I R
5. R E F R I G E R A T O R
6. S I N K
7. O V E N

ROW, ROW, ROW (page 42)

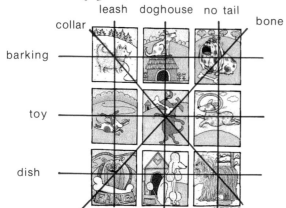

collar leash doghouse no tail bone
barking
toy
dish

INSTANT PICTURE (page 43)

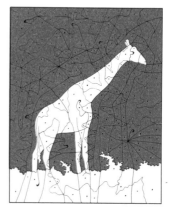

HORROR IN THE OPERA (pages 44-45)

WHO AM I? (page 46)

King Arthur

GLOBE PROBE (pages 16-17)

3. Belize
5. Dominican Republic
6. Zimbabwe
1. France
9. Congo
7. Iraq
4. Iran
2. Thailand
8. Taiwan

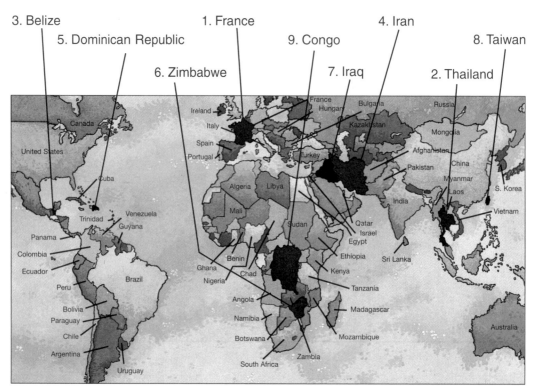